leapfrog
World
Tales

KT-465-604

Chief Five Heads

A Southern African tale
told by Margaret Nash

Illustrated by Anni Axworthy

W

FRANKLIN WATTS

First published in 2009 by
Franklin Watts
338 Euston Road
London
NW1 3BH

Franklin Watts Australia
Level 17/207 Kent Street
Sydney
NSW 2000

Text © Margaret Nash 2009
Illustration © Anni Axworthy 2009

A CIP catalogue record for this book is available
from the British Library.

ISBN 978 0 7496 8593 5 (hbk)
ISBN 978 0 7496 8599 7 (pbk)

Series Editor: Jackie Hamley
Series Advisor: Dr Barrie Wade
Series Designer: Peter Scoulding

Printed in China

Franklin Watts is a division of
Hachette Children's Books,
an Hachette UK company
www.hachette.co.uk

This tale comes from
Southern Africa. Can you
find this area on a map?

Once upon a time, a father
told his daughters of a chief
who wanted a wife.

"I should be the wife of a chief!" said the elder daughter. And she left.

Soon she met a mouse. "Shall I show you the way?" he asked.

"Go away! I am too important to talk to a mouse!" the girl shouted.

Then she met an old
woman who started
to say something.

The girl would not listen
to her and walked away
as fast as she could.

Next she met a hungry goat-boy. "May I have some food?" he asked.

"NO!" she snapped at him, finishing her lunch.

At the village, the chief's sister told her, "Don't be scared of my brother."

"I'm not scared of anything!" laughed the girl rudely.

That night, the wind
howled. The chief blew in!

He was an ugly snake
with five heads. The girl
ran away screaming.

The elder daughter
trudged home.

"Now I will go," said the
younger daughter.

Soon she met a mouse. "Shall I show you the way?" he asked.

"Yes, please," said the girl.

Next she met an old woman. "Take the little path," she said.

"Thank you," said the girl.

Then she met a hungry goat-boy. "May I have some food?" he asked. "Of course," said the girl.

"Be kind to the woman by the stream," he told her. "I shall," said the girl.

By the stream, the girl met the chief's sister. "Don't be scared of my brother," she said.

"I shall not be scared.
Thank you," said the girl.

That night, the wind
howled. In blew the chief.
The girl smiled bravely.

"I saw how kind you were," he said, "for I was the mouse, the old woman and the goat-boy."

Then Chief Five Heads
became a handsome
young man.

And he and the younger
daughter lived happily
ever after.

Puzzle 1

a

b

c

d

e

f

Put these pictures in the correct order.
Now tell the story in your own words.
What different endings can you think of?

Puzzle 2

gentle   polite
bad-tempered

nasty   generous
mean

wise   careful
silly

Choose the correct adjectives for each character. Which adjectives are incorrect? Turn over to find the answers.

Answers

Puzzle 1

The correct order is: 1c, 2f, 3a, 4b, 5d, 6e

Puzzle 2

Elder daughter: the correct adjective is bad-tempered

The incorrect adjectives are gentle, polite

Younger daughter: the correct adjective is generous

The incorrect adjectives are mean, nasty

The chief: the correct adjectives are careful, wise

The incorrect adjective is silly

Look out for Leapfrog fairy tales:

Cinderella
ISBN 978 0 7496 4228 0

The Three Little Pigs
ISBN 978 0 7496 4227 3

Jack and the Beanstalk
ISBN 978 0 7496 4229 7

The Three Billy Goats Gruff
ISBN 978 0 7496 4226 6

Goldilocks and the Three Bears
ISBN 978 0 7496 4225 9

Little Red Riding Hood
ISBN 978 0 7496 4224 2

Rapunzel
ISBN 978 0 7496 6159 5

Snow White
ISBN 978 0 7496 6161 8

The Emperor's New Clothes
ISBN 978 0 7496 6163 2

The Pied Piper of Hamelin
ISBN 978 0 7496 6164 9

Hansel and Gretel
ISBN 978 0 7496 6162 5

The Sleeping Beauty
ISBN 978 0 7496 6160 1

Rumpelstiltskin
ISBN 978 0 7496 6165 6

The Ugly Duckling
ISBN 978 0 7496 6166 3

Puss in Boots
ISBN 978 0 7496 6167 0

The Frog Prince
ISBN 978 0 7496 6168 7

The Princess and the Pea
ISBN 978 0 7496 6169 4

Dick Whittington
ISBN 978 0 7496 6170 0

The Little Match Girl
ISBN 978 0 7496 6582 1

The Elves and the Shoemaker
ISBN 978 0 7496 6581 4

The Little Mermaid
ISBN 978 0 7496 6583 8

The Little Red Hen
ISBN 978 0 7496 6585 2

The Nightingale
ISBN 978 0 7496 6586 9

Thumbelina
ISBN 978 0 7496 6587 6

For more Leapfrog books go to: www.franklinwatts.co.uk